4 Beloved Tales

# SNOW WHITE

## Stories Around the World

by Jessica Gunderson

# What is a fairy tale?

Once upon a time, before the age of books, people gathered to tell stories. They told tales of fairies and magic, princes and witches. Ideas of love, jealousy, kindness and luck filled the stories. Some provided lessons. Others simply entertained. Most did both! These fairy tales passed from neighbour to neighbour, village to village, land to land. As the stories spun across seas and over mountains, details changed to fit each culture. A poisoned slipper became a poisoned ring. A king became a sultan. A wolf became a tiger.

Over time, fairy tales were collected and written down. Around the world today, people of all ages love to read or listen to these timeless stories. For many years to come, fairy tales will continue to live happily ever after in our imaginations.

# Snow White
## A German fairy tale
### illustrated by Eva Montanari

Once upon a time, there lived a beautiful princess called Snow White. Her stepmother, the queen, was also very beautiful. She often gazed into her magical mirror and asked, "Mirror on the wall, who's the fairest of all?"

The mirror always replied, "You."

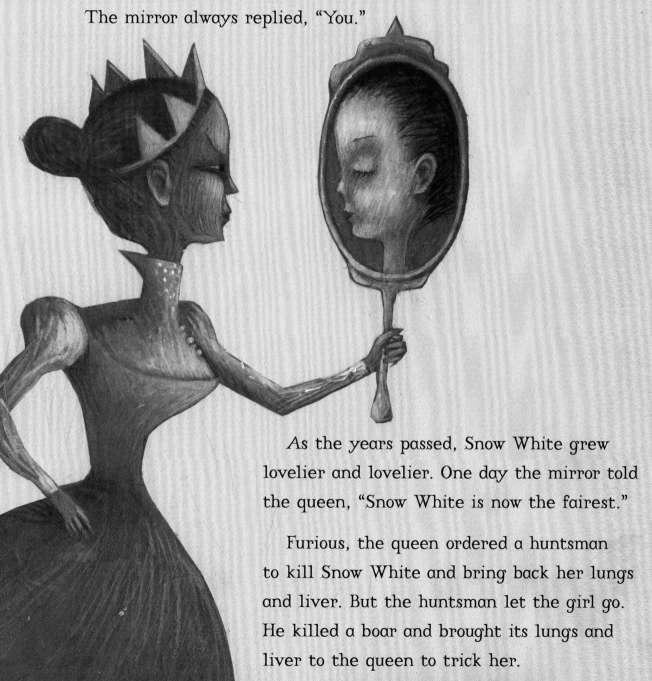

As the years passed, Snow White grew lovelier and lovelier. One day the mirror told the queen, "Snow White is now the fairest."

Furious, the queen ordered a huntsman to kill Snow White and bring back her lungs and liver. But the huntsman let the girl go. He killed a boar and brought its lungs and liver to the queen to trick her.

3

Snow White found a cottage belonging to seven dwarfs. The dwarfs invited her to live with them. In return for their kindness, she cooked and cleaned.

Meanwhile, the mirror told the queen that Snow White still lived. Filled with anger she disguised herself as a merchant and went to the dwarfs' cottage.

Snow White loved the dresses the merchant had for sale. But when she tried one on, the magical laces pulled too tightly. Snow White couldn't breathe. She fell down dead.

With Snow White dead, the queen happily asked the mirror who was the fairest. The mirror replied, "Snow White."

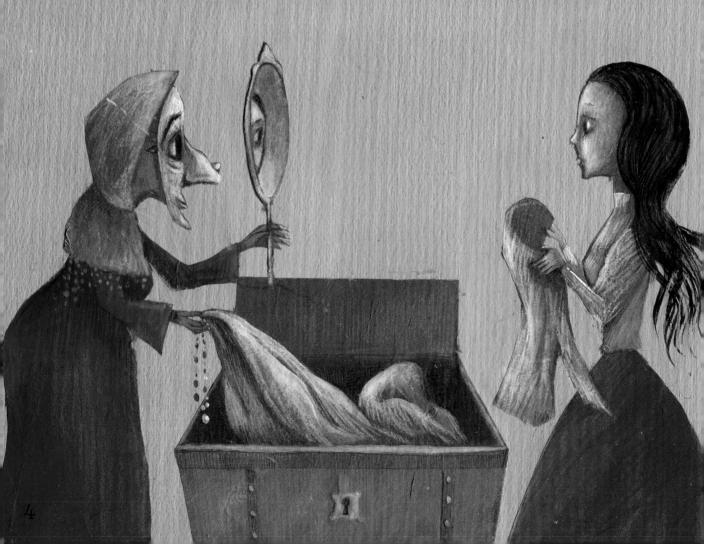

The queen fumed. The dwarfs had
returned home and loosened the laces.
Snow White had come back to life!

The next day the queen went
back to the cottage with a
poisoned comb. *As soon as*
Snow White put it in
her hair, she fell
down dead.

5

Sure of her success, the queen returned home and asked the mirror who was the fairest. It again replied, "Snow White." The dwarfs had found Snow White lifeless and removed the comb.

"Curses!" the queen cried. She poisoned an apple and went back to the cottage.

Snow White was hungry, and the apple looked so good! As soon as she bit into it, she fell down dead.

This time, the dwarfs couldn't help Snow White. There were no laces to loosen and no comb to remove. Saddened, they put her in a glass coffin in their garden.

Back at the castle, the
queen questioned the mirror.
It answered, "You are fairest."
The queen cackled with glee.

One day, a handsome prince saw Snow White and fell in love with her beauty. His servants carried her coffin to his home. On the way, however, the servants tripped. A bit of poisoned apple flew from Snow White's mouth. She opened her eyes and instantly fell in love with the prince. They decided to marry.

About this same time, the queen asked the mirror who was the fairest. The mirror replied, "The prince's bride."

The queen dashed to the prince's wedding. She had to see the bride for herself.

When the queen arrived, Snow White saw her and sounded the alarm. The prince's guards grabbed the queen and put a pair of sizzling-hot iron shoes on her feet. She danced until she fell over dead.

The prince and Snow White lived happily ever after.

# Marigo of the 40 Dragons

## An Albanian fairy tale

illustrated by
Colleen Madden

Once there lived a beautiful princess called
Marigo. She was sweet and had everything.

Her schoolteacher envied her royal life.
One day, she tricked Marigo into killing the
queen. Then she said, "Tell your father
to marry me." Marigo did, and the king
married the schoolteacher.

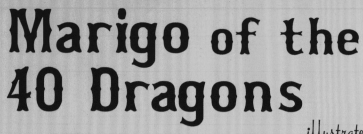

But Marigo's new stepmother still wasn't happy. She grew so jealous of Marigo's beauty that she ordered the king to kill her. The king took his daughter into the mountains, but he couldn't kill her. He left her there, alone.

Marigo found a castle belonging to 40 dragons. At first she was frightened. But she soon discovered the dragons were very kind. She offered to clean their castle in exchange for a place to live.

Back at the king's castle, Marigo's wicked stepmother spoke to the sun. "Is anyone more beautiful than I?" she asked. The sun replied, "Yes. Marigo of the 40 Dragons."

The queen screamed. Marigo was alive! The queen poisoned a hairpin and ordered the king to take it to his daughter. Disguised as a merchant, the king did as his wife ordered.

Marigo felt sorry for the poor merchant and bought the hairpin. She stuck it in her hair and fell down dead.

The dragons came home to find Marigo lifeless. "What is this?" one dragon growled. He yanked the hairpin from her hair, and Marigo came back to life.

Meanwhile, the queen again asked the sun, "Is anyone more beautiful than I?" And the sun replied, "Marigo." The furious queen ordered the king to take a poisoned ring to the princess. The king disguised himself and scurried off.

Marigo again felt sorry for the pitiful merchant and bought the ring. When she put it on, she fell down dead.

The dragons didn't see the ring and couldn't wake her. They built her a glass coffin and hung it in the garden of a young king.

When the young king saw Marigo, he fell in love. He carried her coffin into his palace for safe keeping. One day, his mother saw the ring on the girl's finger. She slipped it off, and Marigo sat up. "Where am I?" she asked, blinking her eyes.

The overjoyed king kissed her. "In a royal palace!" he said. "I am king, and you will be my queen!"

The young king and queen still live happily to this day.

# The Unnatural Mother and the Girl with a Star on Her Forehead
## A Mozambican fairy tale
*illustrated by Carolina Farías*

Once upon a time, there lived a chief's wife with a moon on her forehead. She loved to look into her mirror and ask, "Mirror, is anyone more beautiful?" The mirror always replied, "Only heaven is more beautiful."

Soon the woman gave birth to a daughter. The girl had a star on her forehead. The entire village admired the girl's beauty. But the mother was jealous.

The next time the woman asked the mirror her question, the answer changed. "Only your dear daughter, who came from the heavens," the mirror said. Enraged, the woman smashed the mirror.

Day by day the woman's jealousy grew. It grew so great that she asked her servants to kill the child. If they brought back the girl's heart, liver and little finger, she promised to give them a bag of coins.

But the servants could not bear to kill the girl. They told her to run away. "But first we need to cut off your little finger," they said. After the deed was done, she ran far away. The servants brought back the little finger and an antelope's heart and liver. The chief's wife was happy.

Meanwhile, the girl found a hut that belonged to a gang of thieves. Her beauty charmed the leader. He adopted her and promised to stop stealing.

One day, a passing servant saw the girl's star and told the girl's mother. The evil woman sent him back to the thieves' hut with a pair of poisoned slippers. When the girl put on the slippers, she fell down dead.

Greatly saddened, her
adoptive father built a coffin.
He strung it high up in the
trees. Even though the girl was
dead, her star still glowed.

A chief's son from another village saw the light from the girl's star and fell in love. He took the coffin home. One day his brother visited and admired the girl's slippers. He took them off her feet, and the girl came back to life.

The chief's son was overjoyed. He married the girl and held a feast. Shortly after, he went on a safari. When he returned many months later, a great surprise awaited him. He was the father of twins – a boy with a moon on his forehead and a girl with a star! Together they all lived happily ever after.

23

# The Magic Needle

## A Turkish fairy tale

*illustrated by Valentina Belloni*

Once there lived a padishah who had a beautiful wife and daughter. Each day, the woman asked her servant, "Am I beautiful?" The servant always replied, "Yes, the most beautiful."

One day, however, the servant saw the padishah's lovely daughter, Grenatchen. The next time the wife asked her question, the servant's answer changed. "Yes," he replied. "But Grenatchen is most beautiful."

Upset, the wife took Grenatchen to the wilderness and left her. She hoped wild beasts would eat the girl.

Grenatchen wandered alone until three hunters took her in. News of her beauty spread quickly. The padishah's wife heard the stories. She knew the girl was Grenatchen. She bought two poisoned needles from a witch, disguised herself, and went to the hunters' house.

Grenatchen refused to open the door to a stranger. So the wife said, "Kneel by the keyhole. I will slide lovely hairpins through." Grenatchen kneeled, and the wife pushed both needles into her forehead. The girl fell down dead.

The hunters built Grenatchen a coffin and carried it into the mountains. They strung it between two trees. One day a sultan's son called Schehzade discovered it. Although he was promised to another woman, he fell in love with Grenatchen. He carried her coffin to his palace.

Schehzade married and then went off to war. While he was away, his wife opened the coffin. She pulled one needle from Grenatchen's head.

The dead girl turned into a bird! Every morning it flew to the garden and asked the gardener about Schehzade. When Schehzade came home, the gardener told him about the bird. Curious, Schehzade set a trap and caught it.

Schehzade's jealous wife knew the bird was Grenatchen. She ripped off the bird's head and threw its body into the garden. Rosebushes grew from the bird's blood.

One day an old woman plucked roses from one of the bushes. When she sniffed the petals, a bird popped out and fluttered over her. She noticed a needle in the bird's head and pulled it out. The bird turned into the beautiful Grenatchen.

Grenatchen told the woman her story, and the woman ran to tell Schehzade. Filled with joy, he rushed to Grenatchen.

Meanwhile, the padishah's wife heard that Grenatchen was alive. Determined to kill her again, the woman disguised herself and set out for the sultan's palace.

Schehzade and Grenatchen saw a woman coming towards them. Grenatchen recognized her as the padishah's wife. Schehzade grabbed her and sent her to prison. He put his own wife in prison too.

At last, he and Grenatchen could be married.

# Glossary

**boar** wild pig

**culture** people's way of life, ideas, art, customs and traditions.

**disguise** hide by looking like something else

**merchant** someone who sells goods

**padishah** great king or ruler

**safari** journey for hunting or exploring, usually in Africa

**sultan** ruler or emperor, especially in Muslim countries

# Comprehension questions

Find unique cultural elements of each story. How do these elements fit each culture or country?

Each of the Snow White stories has a jealous mother or stepmother. What makes each one jealous? How does her jealousy affect her actions? What happens to her in the end?

Look at the endings of each of the stories. Are the endings similar or different? Explain your answer.

## Writing prompts

1) Write a Snow White story set where you live. Use details that help identify the place and time of the story (e.g., roads, parks, shops or buildings, people, clothing).

2) Imagine the four Snow Whites meet. Write the conversation they might have. Use dialogue and description to tell the story.

# Read more

**Grimm's Fairy Tales** (Usborne Illustrated),
retold by Ruth Brocklehurst & Gillian Doherty
(Usborne Publishing Ltd, 2011)

**Snow White and the Seven Dwarfs**, Leslie Sims
(Usborne Publishing Ltd, 2005)

**The Tree of Life: An Amazon Folk Tale** (Folk Tales from
Around the World), Charlotte Guillain (Raintree, 2014)

# Website

www.booktrust.org.uk/books/children/
illustrators/illustrations-in-search-of-a-
story/

Make your own book with Chris Riddell!

Raintree is an imprint of Capstone Global Library Limited, a company incorporated in England and Wales having its registered office at 264 Banbury Road, Oxford, OX2 7DY – Registered company number: 6695582

www.raintree.co.uk
myorders@raintree.co.uk

Editor: Jill Kalz
Designer: Ashlee Suker
Art Director: Nathan Gassman
Production Specialist: Katy LaVigne
The illustrations in this book were created digitally.

Printed in China
ISBN 978 1 4747 2417 3
20 19 18 17 16
10 9 8 7 6 5 4 3 2 1

**British Library Cataloguing in Publication Data**
A full catalogue record for this book is available from the British Library.

**Acknowledgements**
Thanks to our advisers for their expertise and advice:

Maria Tatar, PhD, Chair, Program in Folklore & Mythology
John L. Loeb Professor of Germanic Languages & Literatures and Folklore & Mythology, Harvard University

Terry Flaherty, PhD, Professor of English
Minnesota State University, Mankato

Every effort has been made to contact copyright holders of material reproduced in this book. Any omissions will be rectified in subsequent printings if notice is given to the publisher.

All the Internet addresses (URLs) given in this book were valid at the time of going to press. However, due to the dynamic nature of the Internet, some addresses may have changed, or sites may have changed or ceased to exist since publication. While the author and publisher regret any inconvenience this may cause readers, no responsibility for any such changes can be accepted by either the author or the publisher.

# Look out for all the books in this series: